GARFIELD

TREASURY 5

JIM DAVIS

ℛℛ

RAVETTE PUBLISHING

This edition first published by Ravette Publishing Limited 2004.

Printed and bound in Singapore
for Ravette Publishing Limited,
Unit 3, Tristar Centre,
Star Road, Partridge Green,
West Sussex RH13 8RA

ISBN: 1 84161 198 0

ENJOY THE LITTLE THINGS, AND THE BIG THINGS WILL TAKE CARE OF THEMSELVES

JIM DAVIS 3-18

IF YOU THINK YOU'RE PSYCHING ME OUT, YOU'RE MISTAKEN

JIM DAVIS 3-17

BOOT!

www.garfield.com

© 2002 PAWS, INC. All Rights Reserved.

STUPID HEAD WIND

JiM DAViS 4-14

© 2002 PAWS, INC. All Rights Reserved.

Other GARFIELD titles published by Ravette ...

Pocket Books

	ISBN	Price
Below Par	1 84161 152 2	£3.50
Bon Appetit	1 84161 038 0	£3.50
Compute This!	1 84161 194 8	£3.50
Double Trouble	1 84161 008 9	£3.50
Eat My Dust	1 84161 098 4	£3.50
Fun in the Sun	1 84161 097 6	£3.50
Goooooal!	1 84161 037 2	£3.50
Great Impressions	1 85304 191 2	£3.50
I Don't Do Perky	1 84161 195 6	£3.50
In Training	1 85304 785 6	£3.50
Light Of My Life	1 85304 353 2	£3.50
On The Right Track	1 85304 907 7	£3.50
Pop Star	1 84161 151 4	£3.50
To Eat, Or Not To Eat?	1 85304 991 3	£3.50
With Love From Me To You	1 85304 392 3	£3.50

Theme Books

		ISBN	Price
Behaving Badly		1 85304 892 5	£4.50
Cat Napping		1 84161 087 9	£4.50
Coffee Mornings		1 84161 086 0	£4.50
Creatures Great & Small		1 85304 998 0	£3.99
Healthy Living		1 85304 972 7	£3.99
Pigging Out		1 85304 893 3	£4.50
Successful Living		1 85304 973 5	£3.99
The Seasons		1 85304 999 9	£3.99
Entertains You	(new)	1 84161 221 9	£4.50
Slam Dunk!	(new)	1 84161 222 7	£4.50

2-in-1 Theme Books

		ISBN	Price
Easy Does It		1 84161 191 3	£6.99
Licensed to Thrill		1 84161 192 1	£6.99
The Gruesome Twosome		1 84161 143 3	£6.99
Out For The Couch		1 84161 144 1	£6.99
Lazy Daze	(new)	1 84161 208 1	£6.99
All In Good Taste	(new)	1 84161 209 X	£6.99

Classic Collections

		ISBN	Price
Volume One		1 85304 970 0	£5.99
Volume Two		1 85304 971 9	£5.99
Volume Three		1 85304 996 4	£5.99
Volume Four		1 85304 997 2	£5.99
Volume Five		1 84161 022 4	£5.99
Volume Six		1 84161 023 2	£5.99
Volume Seven		1 84161 088 7	£5.99
Volume Eight		1 84161 089 5	£5.99
Volume Nine		1 84161 149 2	£5.99
Volume Ten		1 84161 150 6	£5.99
Volume Eleven		1 84161 175 1	£5.99
Volume Twelve		1 84161 176 X	£5.99
Volume Thirteen	(new)	1 84161 206 5	£5.99
Volume Fourteen	(new)	1 84161 207 3	£5.99

Little Books

	ISBN	Price
C-c-c-caffeine	1 84161 183 2	£2.50
Food 'n' Fitness	1 84161 145 X	£2.50
Laughs	1 84161 146 8	£2.50
Love 'n' Stuff	1 84161 147 6	£2.50
Surf 'n' Sun	1 84161 186 7	£2.50
The Office	1 84161 184 0	£2.50
Wit 'n' Wisdom	1 84161 148 4	£2.50
Zzzzzzz	1 84161 185 9	£2.50

Miscellaneous

		ISBN	Price
Garfield The Movie	(new)	1 84161 205 7	£7.99
Garfield 25 years of me!		1 84161 173 5	£7.99
Treasury 4		1 84161 180 8	£10.99
Treasury 3		1 84161 142 5	£9.99

All Garfield books are available at your local bookshop or from the publisher at the address below. Just tick the titles required and send the form with your payment and name and address details to:

RAVETTE PUBLISHING, Unit 3, Tristar Centre, Star Road, Partridge Green, West Sussex RH13 8RA

Prices and availability are subject to change without prior notice.

Please enclose a cheque or postal order made payable to Ravette Publishing to the value of the cover price of the book and allow the following for UK p&p:-

60p for the first book + 30p for each additional book, except Garfield Treasuries, when please add £3.00 per copy.